Horizons

Ann's Cat

Horizons
Phonics and Reading K
Reader 1

Author: Pollyann O'Brien, M.A.

Editor: Alan L. Christopherson, M.S.

Illustrations: Cynthia Cox, A.A.
Karen Eubanks, B.A.
Dawn Tessier, B.A.

Alpha Omega Publications • Rock Rapids, IA

Printed in the United States of America

ISBN 978-0-7403-0141-4

A Note to Teachers and Parents

The Horizons Kindergarten Phonics Readers are to be used as a companion to the Horizons Kindergarten Phonics Student Workbooks. For each lesson in the Student Workbooks there is a corresponding story in the Readers. The story will illustrate and demonstrate the primary concept of the lesson. Most kindergarten students should not be expected to read these stories independently. The stories include a mixture of simple short-vowel words and more complex multi-syllable or long-vowel words. The teacher or parent should read the stories to the student, pausing where appropriate to allow the student to sound out and read the words they have covered in the lessons. As the student's vocabulary increases, the teacher or parent is encouraged to repeat the Reader stories in a cyclic fashion. For example; on the day "x" is covered (Lesson 26) both the "x" story and the "short a" story (Lesson 1) can be read.

It is important to ask questions both before and after reading the story. Talk about things to look for or to expect in the story based upon the title or the illustrations. Comprehension questions are included at the end of each story beginning with Lesson 27.

The ability to sound out and read words varies with each individual student. They are in the early stages of learning a skill that they will continue to develop for the rest of their lives. So, have fun, enjoy the stories and keep in mind that it is not necessary that every student sound out and read every word.

Table of Contents

ANN'S CAT

This is Ann

Ann has a cat.

The cat is fat.

The cat ran and ran.

Ann ran and ran.

Ann and the cat ran.

THE BUG BAG

Abby has a big bag.

Abby has a big bug.

Abby put the bug in the bag.

The bug is not happy.

DAD'S CAT

This is Dad.

Dad put the cat on the mat.

The cat is happy on the mat.

Dad is as happy as the cat.

DON'S BIG DOG

Don has a dog.

Don's dog is big.

Don is little.

Don is not big.

Don has a cot.

Don's dog sat on the cot.

The big dog is too big for the cot.

Look at the cot.

Don put the dog on a mat.

The cot is for Don.

CAL'S CAP

Cal has a cap.

Cal's cap is big.

Cal's cap is red.

Cal put his cap on the cot.

The cat sat on Cal's cap.

BEN

Ben has a cat.

Ben has a dog.

Ben put the cat on the mat.

Ben put the dog on the mat.

Ben sat on the mat.

Ben sat on the mat with the cat and dog.

Ben had a rest with the cat and dog.

THE FOX

This is a fox.

The fox is fat.

The fox sat in the den.

The fox saw a cat.

The cat saw the fox.

Wow! The cat ran.

The cat ran fast.

The cat ran back to his mat.

THE VAN

This is Dad's van.

Dad's van is tan.

Dad ran to the van.

Jan ran to the van.

Dad had to get gas for the van.

The van ran better with gas.

THE TWINS

Jill and Jim are twins.

Jill and Jim are six.

Jim has a red cap.

Jill has a red hat.

Jim can jump.

Jill can jig.

Jim and Jill are happy twins.

Hal Fell

Hal sat on the bed.

Hal fell off the bed.

Hal got up.

Hal is not sad.

He did not hit his hand.

He did not hit his head.

He will get back on the bed.

He will not fall off the bed this time.

JUDD AND BUZZ

Judd is an umpire.

Judd says, "Get up to bat, Buzz."

Buzz has a bat.

Buzz has a big bat.

Bob can toss the ball to Buzz.

Buzz hit the ball.

The ball went up, up, up.

Up, up, up went the ball.

The ball went up and over.

Judd says, "Good hit, Buzz.
You did a good job."

A TOOTH

Tom and Tim are twins.

The twins are ten years old.

Tom has lost one tooth.

Tom put his tooth in a cup.

Oh, Oh! The cup will tip over on the table.

Tim has lost one tooth.

Tim put his tooth in a tin can.

Oh, Oh! The tin can will tip over.

Tim's tooth is on the table, too.

THE FISH NET

Ned's net is on the table.

Ned will put the net in his bag.

Ned can go to the pond.

Ned can go to the pond to fish.

The net will help Ned get fish.

Ned will put the net in the pond.

Ten fish can see the net.

Nine fish get away from the net.

Ned has one fish in his net.

KEN'S KITTEN

Ken has a little tan kitten.

The kitten is ill.

The kitten will not purr.

The kitten will not kick.

The kitten will not get up.

Ken will get the vet.

The vet will fix the kitten.

Ken's kitten will get well.

LES CAN LIFT

Les can lift a net.

The net is little.

Les can lift the box.

The box is little.

Les can lift a tub.

The tub is little.

Les cannot lift the dog.

The dog is not little.

The dog is big.

The dog is too big.

Les is too little.

THE MASK

Meg has a mask.

Meg's mask is black.

Meg can put on the mask.

Meg can look in the glass.

"Oh no," said Meg.

"I look like a mutt in this mask."

Meg put the mask in a box.

THE PUPPY

Pat has a pet.

Pat's pet is a tan puppy.

The puppy ran to Pat.

Pat can pet the puppy.

The puppy can wag his tail.

The puppy is happy.

The puppy is happy to be Pat's pet.

Pat is happy with his pet puppy.

THE RAG DOLL

The rag doll is on Rod's bed.

Rod says, "I do not want a rag doll.

I do not want a rag doll on my bed.

Get the rag doll off of my bed."

Rod will toss the rag doll on the rug.

Jill says, "This rag doll is on the rug.

She is not happy on the rug."

Jill will pick up the rag doll.

Jill will put the rag doll on her bed.

Now the rag doll is happy.

Jill is happy.

Rod is happy.

THE SOCKS

Sam has three socks.

One sock is red.

One sock is green.

One sock is blue.

"This is not good," said Sam.
"I must get one more red sock.
I must get one more green sock.
I must get one more blue sock.
Then it will be OK."

Sam will look under the bed.
No sock.
Sam will look in back of the box.
Sam will get the lid off of the box.
Sam will look in the box.
Sam says, "Here are my socks.
Now I have two red socks.
I have two blue socks.
I have two green socks.
This is very good."

QUACKER, THE DUCK

Quacker sits on a nest.

A dog will look at the duck.

The dog wants to run with Quacker.

Quacker says, "Quack, quack.

Get out! Get out!"

A cat will look at Quacker.

The cat wants to run with Quacker.

"Quack, quack," says Quacker.

"Get out! Get out! Get out!

I just want to sit on my nest."

THE JACK-IN-THE-BOX

This is Jack.

The jack-in-the-box is Jed's toy.

Jed will put his hand on top of the box.

Up, up, up, pops Jack.

Jed put his hand on Jack's top.

Down, down, down went the

jack-in-the-box.

Down went Jack.

THE VESTS

Mom got Bill a new vest.

Bill's vest is red.

Mom got Rod a new vest.

Rod's vest is blue.

Mom got Ned a new vest.

Ned's vest is green.

Bill put on his new red vest.

Rod put on his new blue vest

Ned put on his new green vest.

Bill and Rod and Ned got in Dad's van.

Dad and Mom got in the van.

The van can get them to the church.

THE BIG WIG

Val saw a box on the bed.

Val saw a wig in a box.

Val will put on the wig.

The wig is too big.

"Oh no," said Val.

"The wig is too big.

I look funny.

I will put the wig back in the box."

THE YO-YO

Jack has a yellow yo-yo.

Bob has a red yo-yo.

Tom did not get a yo-yo.

Tom and Bob are pals.

Bob ran to Tom.

Bob said, "This is my red yo-yo.

Do you want to play with it?"

Tom says, "Yes, I want to play with your
red yo-yo. Thanks."

Jack says, "Do you want to play with the yellow yo-yo?"

Tom says, "Yes, thanks. I want to play with a red yo-yo. I want to play with a yellow yo-yo, too. I am happy."

THE ZOO

Dan is at the zoo.

Dan can see dogs at the zoo.

Dan can see cats at the zoo.

Dan can see pigs at the zoo.

Dan can see monkeys at the zoo.

Best of all, Dan can see the zebra.

Dan said, "The zebra is big.

The zebra is black and white."

Dan is glad he is at the zoo.

Do you like the zoo?

"THE X"

This is an 'X'.
This is a box.

This 'X' is put
under the box.

This is a fox.
The 'X' is put on the front foot of the fox.

This is a six.

6

The 'X' is put on top of the six.

X

This is an 'X'.

This 'X' is in the box.

THAD'S MATH

Thad was in the third grade at school. He liked to read, but math was hard for him. He worked on four plus three. He had to think. Is it six or seven? Yes, I think it is seven. He checked it out with some chips. He was sure he was OK, but it was good to check his answer. "I need some counters," he said.

$$\begin{array}{r} 3 \\ +4 \\ \hline 6 \end{array} \qquad ? \qquad \begin{array}{r} 3 \\ +4 \\ \hline 7 \end{array}$$

Thad took the things out of his desk. "I thought I had a box of thin pencils I could count," he said. He looked and looked. All he could find was one thick eraser. "That will not help me when I count."

Then Thad remembered. He had put the thin pencils in a box on top of the chest.

"Thanks, Good Lord," he said. "You helped me remember where my thin pencils were. Now I can use them to help me count when I do my math."

What did Thad like to do in school?
What was hard for him?
What did he want for counters?
Where did he find them?

A BUBBLE BATH

Beth wanted to take a bath. She said, "Mom, can I have a bubble bath?"

Mom said, "Sure, you can have bubbles in your bath. Do you want the pink bubbles or the orange bubbles? I do not think you want both, do you?"

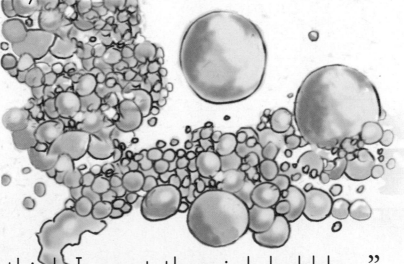

"Oh, I think I want the pink bubbles," Beth said. "I like to blow them all over the bathroom."

Mom fixed Beth's bath with pink bubbles.
I like them both, but I like
the pink ones the best.

Beth hopped in the bath full of pink bubbles. She had bubbles up to her nose. She had bubbles up to her chin. Some of the bubbles got in her mouth.

Beth blew them across the bathroom. "Oh, no," she yelled. "My tooth was loose and I blew it out with the bubbles."

What did Beth want to do?
What color of bubbles did she choose?
How deep were the bubbles?
What happened when Beth blew the bubbles away?

THE CHAMP

Jack Black is a champ. He is a champ in math. Jack is always at the top in his class. Jack is champ on the ranch, too.

But Jack was sad. He said, "I can just splash in the water. I want to swim."

Frank said, "I will be glad to help you swim. But you will have to make me a math champ, too."

Thank you," said Jack. "That is what I will do."

Jack helped Frank cram for his math test.

Frank helped Jack do more than just splash in the water.

Soon Frank was a champ in math.

Jack was a champ in the water, too.

Who was the math class champ?
What did Jack want to learn to do?
Who said they would help Jack swim?
What did Jack have to do for Frank?
Who was a champ in the water?

KEN'S TOY CAR

Ken has a red toy car. It can go fast. The wheels go like a whiz.

Ken sent the toy car across the desk to Ann. Ann held it in her hands. Then she sent the toy car back to Ken with a wham!

Ken said, "Be careful with my car.
Do not wham it into the desk.
This is the best toy car."

"Sorry," said Ann. "I will be careful."

One day Ken lost his toy car. He felt sad. He asked Mom to help him look for it.

"Where did you play with it last?" Mom asked.

"I do not remember where I put it," said Ken.

Mom helped look for it. They looked in the hen pen. They looked for it under the bed. They looked for it by the steps. At last Ken felt under the desk.

"Yes," he yelled. "This is my red car! This is my car that can go like a whiz."

Ken felt great.

What color was Ken's car?
Who played with Ken?
Why did Ken get sad?
Who helped Ken look for his car?
Where did they find the car?

CHUCK'S FISH

Chuck and Rick are Rat pals. Chuck is a big black rat. Chuck is fat. Rick is a long, thin rat with a hat. Rick is not black. He is a white rat.

Chuck said, "I wish I had a fish."

Rick said, "I will get a fish for you. I will get six fish for you."

Rick got his fishing rod. The fish were biting. Rick got one fish fast. He put the fish in a sack.

Kit, the kitten was a pest. She peeked into the sack and hid Rick's fish. Chuck and Rick did not see her. Then she hid the fish in a dish.

Rick got another fish. He put it in his sack.

Kit slipped up to the sack and hid the fish.

Rick was happy fishing. The fish kept biting. Rick said, "Now, we have six fish. Let us take our fish and go home."

Kit hid back of the deck and laughed.
She had hidden all six of Rick's fish.
She was a pest.

Rick said, "Chuck, where are my fish?
There are not any in my sack. I am mad."

"Meow," laughed Kit. "I hid them.
Go and find them."

Chuck and Rick looked in the chest. No
fish. They looked in the tent. No fish.
They looked around the dock. No fish.

Kit laughed, "I think your fish are in the
sack. Look in your sack again."

Rick and Chuck looked in the sack again.
There were the fish. Kit had played a trick
on them. She put the fish back into the sack
when they were not looking.

"You are a pest," said Chuck. "You are a tricky pest, but it was a fun trick. Thanks. I am glad we have our fish."

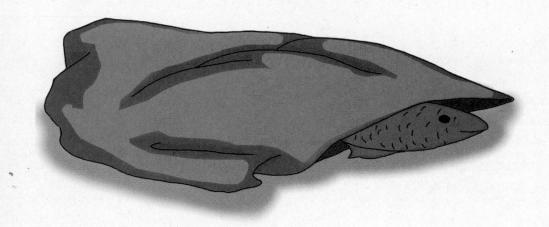

What does Rick look like?
What does Chuck want?
What did Rick do for him?
What did Kit do for a trick?
Where did they find the fish?

SHAD'S TOY SHIP

Shad said, "Dad, could I go to the old shack and look around?"

Dad said, "Yes, Shad, that would be OK. There is a big chest in the shack, and you could find some toys you would like. I will be here in the shop if you want me."

"Thanks, Dad," said Shad. Off he ran to look inside the chest in the old shack. When he got there, he saw the chest. It did not have a lock on it. Shad lifted the lid. There he saw lots of things in the chest.

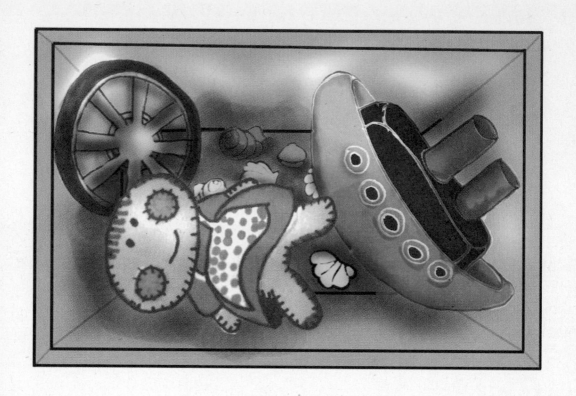

Shad saw six pretty shells with many shapes. He saw a wheel for a bike. There was a little girl's doll. Then he saw a toy ship. He picked it up and looked at it.

"This should be fun to have with my toys," he said. "I like it." Shad shut the lid on the chest and ran back to the shop where Dad was shifting boxes around.

Shad said, "This is a good ship, Dad. Thanks for telling me about it. I will keep it with my toys."

Where did Shad want to go?
What was the first thing Shad saw?
What did he like the best?
Where was Shad going to keep it?

SHELLY'S WISH

Shelly and Sally went to the wishing well.
They each had ten pennies in cash.

Shelly said, "What would happen if I put
all ten pennies in the wishing well?
Would I get my wish?"

"What are your wishes?" asked Sally.

"Oh," said Shelly, "I wish for a lot of things. I want a little pink pig for a pet."

"That is a pretty silly wish," said Sally. "I do not think that wish would ever come true. Pink pigs do not come out of a wishing well."

"If I had a pig, I would give him fresh squash and mash it up for him," answered Shelly.

"What else do you want when you make your wish," asked Sally.

"Maybe I should wish for a kitten," said Shelly.

"I think that is a good plan," said Sally. "Wishing well wishes are just stories. It is just fun to think about it."

Shelly said, "I think I will save my cash and get a kitten."

What was Shelly's first wish?
What was Shelly's second wish?
Do wishing well wishes come true?
How can Shelly get a kitten?

HELP FOR A CHICK

One day a little chick got out of his nest.
He got too close to the chips of wood. The
chips were made for the fire—not for a
baby chick to shift around. The chick was
pushing chips all over and trying to get out.

The baby chick yelled for help. Chet heard the chick chirping for help. "I should check this out," he said.

When Chet got there, he saw the chick thrashing around in the chips. Chet picked up the chick.

"I think I should take him back to the shed," said Chet. "That is where his nest is, and that is where the chick should be."

What happened to the chick?
What was he doing?
Who came to help the chick?
Where did the chick have to go?

KATE'S POCKET

"Hello. My name is Kate.
Look at my name on my
pocket," said Kate.
"I have a pocket full of
gifts."

Kate was at a baseball game.

Kate saw Nan.
Nan was a little girl.
Nan looked sad.
Kate opened her pocket.
She gave a doll to Nan.

Kate met Jake. Jake plays baseball.

Kate gave some gum to Jake.

Kate met Dave.

Dave was at the baseball game, too.

Dave was the umpire at the game.

Kate had a baseball cap for Dave.

Kate said, "Look in my pocket. It is empty."

Who had a pocket full of gifts?
What did Kate give to Nan?
What did she give to Jake?
What did she do for Dave, the umpire?
How did her pocket look then?

WHERE TO SIT

Blake wanted to see a baseball team. He wanted to see the players blaze into first base. Blake looked for a seat where he could sit down. He went to the bleachers. All the seats were full.

Blake went to look for a place to sit in the shade. There was a sign that said: DO NOT SIT HERE IN THE SHADE. No, Blake could not sit in the shade.

Blake went to the gate. There was a sign that said: DO NOT SIT ON THE GATE. No, Blake could not sit on the gate.

Blake went to the cake stand. It was Jane's ice cream, cake and shake stand.
There was a sign that said:
BUY OUR SHAKES AND CAKES.
No, Blake could not sit there.

Then Blake went to the crates.
There was a sign that said:
DO NOT SIT ON THE CRATES.
No, Blake could not sit on the crates.

Jane saw Blake looking for a place to sit.

She said, "My name is 'Jane.'

Come and sit here. I can see that you want to see the players blast the ball over first base."

Blake said, "Thanks.

I'll buy one of your cakes.
Then I'll sit here.
This place is the best. I bless
you for it."

What did Blake want to see?
Where did Blake go first to find a place to sit down?
What did the sign say?
Where did Blake get to sit to watch the game?

NO SNAKES FOR ME

Bret wanted to go swimming. He had to go over the bridge to get to the lake. He had asked his pal, Brant, to go with him. They were going to meet at the bridge.

Bret's mom had made a cake for him to take. Brant was going to bring some bread and jam so they could have a picnic.

Bret and Brant ate their cake and bread. It was a good picnic.

Then they had a race to the lake. "Look out!" yelled Brant. There is a snake in the brush."

Bret came close to the snake.

Brant said, "Let us go home – and fast. I do not want to swim with a snake."

What did Brant want to do?
Who was going to meet him at the bridge?
What did they have to eat for their picnic?
Why did they go home so fast?

COOL OFF

Clay was part of a club. The club went hiking to the shore each week. Clay and Sam looked at the clock. It was time to start their trip to the shore to dig clams.

It was a hot day in July. Clay said, "This day is too hot to dig clams. We will have to cool off first."

Clay got some ice cubes. He put them in a cloth. Then he put the cloth around his neck and chest. Soon the ice cubes had melted and the cloth was wet.

He said, "Sam, do you want me to fix a cloth with some ice to keep you cool?"

"Yes," said Sam. "That would make me cool, too."

Clay and Sam had the wet cloth on their necks and chests. They put some ice in their hands.

Clay said, "My hands are wet, but I am cool."

Sam said, "My hands are wet, too, but I am cool. My neck is cool and my chest is cool. The clams will just have to wait until another day to be dug."

What had Clay and Sam planned to do?
Why did they not do it?
What did they do to cool off?
When were they going to dig clams again?

THE CRAB STORY

Have you ever eaten a crab dinner? Yum – yum! It is good. Have you ever eaten a crab salad? Yum – yum! It is good, too. King crabs and blue crabs are the best to eat.

Did you ever see a crab creeping and crawling on the sand? They run sideways, not to the front like we do.

A crab is an animal that has a hard shell like a flat crate on its back. It lives in sandy waters and also in deep waters. There are many kinds of crabs. A funny kind of a crab is a hermit crab. It crawls inside an empty seashell and uses it for his house.

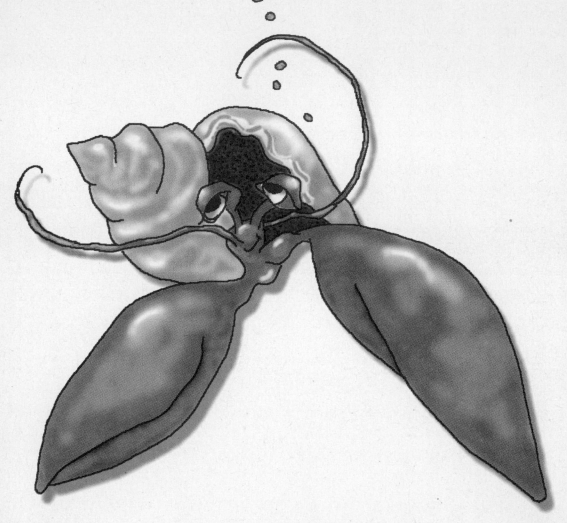

Crabs have four pairs of legs and one pair of claws. The body of the crab shell must be six inches across their flat back before they can be used for food. Their claws are about two inches long and are strong. Do not ever get your fingers in one of the claws. You would feel 'crabby' because it would hurt.

What kind of crabs do people eat?
How does a crab move?
Where does a crab live?
How many pairs of legs do crabs have?

A CROW'S BRUNCH

Brant had seen an old black crow. He was sitting on a branch of a tree near the house. Brant said, "I wish I could bribe him to sit on the bench with me."

Clay said, "Why not take a crust of pie and creep slowly to the tree where he is perching. Maybe you can make friends with him."

"I will fix him some brunch," said Brant. He got a crust of bread and a piece of pie with a sweet crust. He crawled out to the tree where the crow was sitting. Brant tossed the crow's brunch to him.

The old black crow sat and looked at Brant until he got close. Then the crow flew away.

"I guess the old crow did not want any brunch," said Clay. The boys went back to the house and started to play a game called "Crazy 8's."

In the blink of an eye, the old crow was back picking up the brunch. Brant laughed, "Look what he is eating first. He likes crust of the pie better than he likes bread crusts. He is a smart crow."

Where did Brant want the crow to go?
What did Clay say to do?
What did Brant toss to the crow?
What did the crow like the best?